D1585966

Directed by
Ursula MAYER

Screenplay by
Maria FUSCO

GONDA

Sternberg Press

I have no need of your education. You
have taught me less than I knew already,
before I was born even. For this you will
in future times be punished.

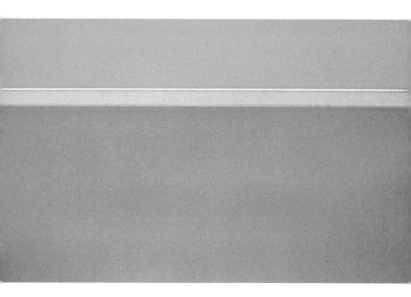

I will not yet specify the exact nature of this amercement. Be assured, your indolence will find its twin in torture.

I have often been disappointed in that
which I was not offered. This is nothing
however, compared to the disappointment
in that which I have been offered.

Oh, and a box of matches.

I know it needs to be done—it's just that
I don't like anyone touching me.

Yes, it's broken down again. Third time
in as many months. And not much more
than a year old. But it clearly says on the
window you close at 5.00 pm. What, earlier
on Thursdays?

This is addressed to me, I am writing to   comma
myself. I am writing and thinking that   full stop
I am speaking to a woman who is the only
justification for the existence of this earth,   comma
and who has the courage to want to be.   full stop
A woman who does not assume the glory
of greatness for just a few hours. A woman   full stop
who seeks that glory in every minute and
every step. A woman in whom life is not   full stop
a curse, nor a bargain, but a hymn.   comma   comma   full stop

full stop

comma
full stop

comma

I want nothing except to know that such
a woman as I exists. So I have written this,   full stop   comma
even though I may not bother to even read
it, or in reading, may not understand.   comma   comma   full stop
I do not know what I am. I am writing to   full stop
what I might become.   full stop

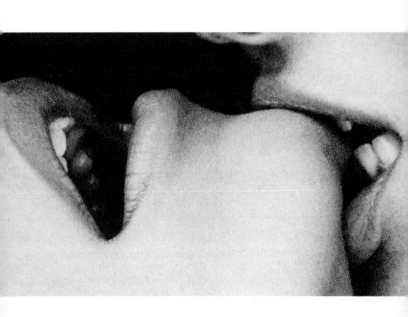

full stop
full stop

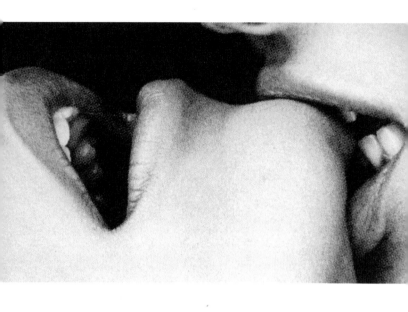

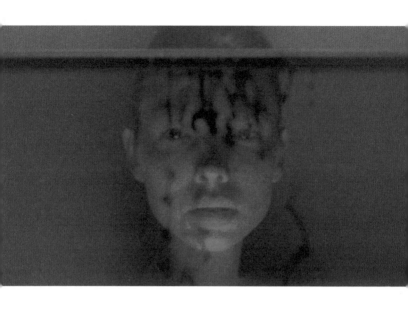

LOSS
CAN'T
GET
IN

I have no need of your education. You
have taught me less than I knew already,
before I was born even.

I am unknown. But I realise to what heights I shall rise, for I carry a banner which cannot fail—a banner which is myself. I have been nothing that was not myself. I stand firm on everything I've done. I have never seen myself. I do not need to. My eyes remain closed.

full stop
comma
em dash
full stop
full stop
full stop   full stop
full stop   full stop

full stop

My face is but a mirror. Someday I shall
hear them speak of me. Until then, this
is but a first tribute—

full stop
full stop   comma
em dash

I have had everything women can ask of life. I have seen it all, and feel as if I were leaving a third-rate show on a disreputable side street. If I do not bother to die, it is only because my life has all the emptiness of the grave and my death would have no change to offer me.

full stop   comma
hyphen
full stop   comma

full stop

It may happen, any day now, and nobody   comma   comma
—not even the one who writes these lines   em dash
—will know the difference. But before   em dash   full stop
it happens, I want to raise what is left   comma
of myself in a last salute. I who am that   full stop
which the world could have been.   full stop

The determinism of duty had conditioned
me to pursue the relief of my fellow
woman's suffering. I see daily before me   full stop
the wrecks and victims of an outrageous
social system. But I gain courage for my   full stop
cause when I look to myself and realise of
what greatness the human race is capable.   full stop

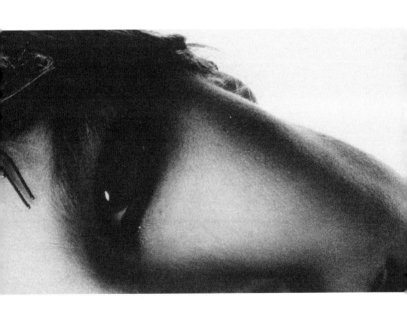

I am the symbol of the hidden potentiality
I see in my derelict sisters. I did not choose   full stop
to be what I am. I did not choose the   full stop
bleak, hopeless life I am forced to lead. But   comma   full stop
in my ability to recognise myself, and to   comma
seem myself, lies all future hope.   comma   full stop

ONLY
THE
ORIGINAL
MEANS

For this you will in future times
be punished.

Arterial
Venereal
Immaterial
Ethereal
Sidereal
Funereal

Last night I dreamt I was dead. Finished as me. Unmade from the world. No. Not right. I have been dead for thirty years. I can see clearly what state I am in. I have left your today, and yet, I am still aware. No. Still not right.

I make to scream, to issue, to swallow
space with my voice. Inhaling, my chest
captures the tawny air surrounding me.
Gulping whole now.

Tepid, spent and acrid. As the passing of a firework. Better. My shriek begins with great force. A well-made squib fired true. Outwards... Towards... But immediately, maybe before I have even begun, the cry fizzles, tapering to a wheeze. Yes.

VOICE
SLAUGHTER

I will not yet specify the exact nature of
this amercement.

Relentless wasn't it?

Yes on and on, rather like reading a
treatise of impossible proportions. It's
clear the original was handwritten,
so it seemed courteous to follow suit.
A peculiar way to do it in these times
no doubt. For someone, you know *like*
her, who wants to *lead* the whole time,
to devise and enforce rules which must
be followed unerringly, to emit such a
personal appeal, written by hand indeed,
could be characterised as unethical.

A collective subjectivity?

A fractured narrative would be
more precise.

Where's the *inside* meaning of it?

Amidst those words was the blink of
possibility, encased in overt description.
An existence that could perhaps escape
her own economy. A refinement.
Liquification without grammar.

A slip?

As disquieting as this may seem, she
was bound to come crashing down on
waves of fantasy that she'd banished
from the clarity of reason; bound to
trample unregulated over the common
people she asserted itself above; bound to
fictionalise; bound to degrade the ending.

Bound to suffer both physically and
spiritually in an effort to achieve purity
and virtue?

No. A human is defined by potential,
not by obedience to template.

In that way her handwriting was future-producing?

Yes. A human cannot alone carry the burden of revolution, it would excise their subjectivity, and place it in the service of fears and anxieties they had not themselves created.

She was tremulous before our questions?

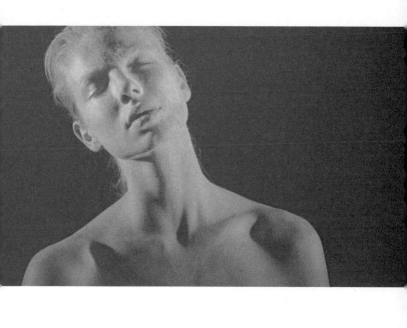
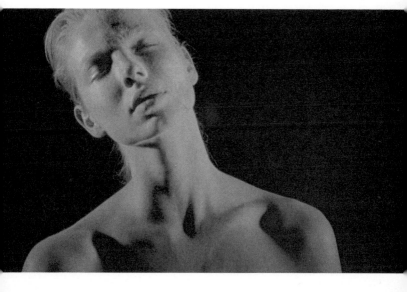

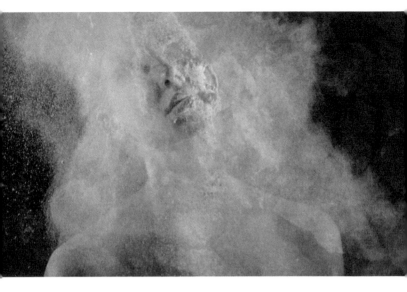

We questioned only *her* surface, humming with the unique intensities emitted from her image.

In time...

In spite of being inorganic, that image became *her* curse through the ways in which *we* related to it, faced it and expressed through it our own pleasures. Such pleasures cannot be adequately described here. Know they are disrespectful of her, of her inherent susceptibility. Remember, our relation with her image makes other images too become inorganic.

I wonder, where is the logic of sentiment?

Why, in the event of love of course: the
negotiation of intimacy and distance.

And our search for this?

The search creates a feeling of complicity
in despair. Madness, love, supplication,
dishevelled joy of communication,
madness, love, not a point in empty
space, madness, love and even more
laughter, dizziness, vertigo, nausea,
madness, love, loss of self to the point
of death, affirmation, madness, love,
reflection and affection for that which
escapes, madness, love.

And the slip of her hand, a justified escape?

Justified. Yes, justified. I'll privilege
abstraction here because it is intensely
material, whereas transcription robs
us of materiality. Abstraction—it's real,
an operation, a way of thinking.

But, what if she simply made a mistake?

No matter. Her fans hid behind their pens, indulging in fantasies and desires, wanting only the imaginary. If their desires had been met, obsession would vanish at once, and the fans' reactions would be brutal, especially towards the object of their dream. Fanaticism may only be sustained through the nonexistence of what dominates the fans' imaginations and thoughts. This is no accident.

They slaughtered her voice?

They populated her sparseness.

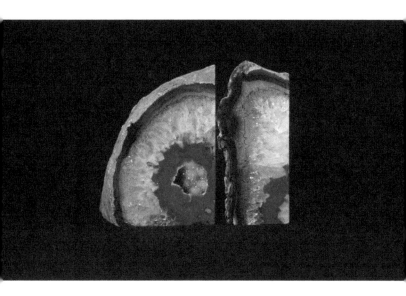

There is something about me I can't give
a name to, something I had and lost, yet   comma   comma
feel as if I'm keeping for myself, for all   comma
of us. I had it long ago, when I was very   full stop   comma
young. I remember how it was: when   full stop   colon
I was young, there was something ahead   comma
of me, so big that I was afraid of it, but   comma   comma
I waited for it and was so happy waiting.   full stop

Then the years passed and it never came.   full stop
And then I found, one day, I wasn't waiting   comma   comma
any longer. It seems foolish, because I   full stop   comma
didn't even know what it was I was waiting
for. I look at myself now and I don't know.   full stop   full stop
But when I look again—I do. You see,   em dash   full stop   comma
I'm still a human being.   full stop

comma
full stop

comma
full stop

full stop

full stop
comma   comma   full stop

full stop   comma

comma   comma   full stop
full stop
full stop

full stop

comma

em dash

full stop

full stop

full stop   full stop

full stop   full stop

full stop

full stop   comma

em dash

full stop   comma

hyphen

full stop   comma

full stop

comma   comma
em dash
em dash   full stop
comma
full stop
full stop
full stop

full stop

full stop

full stop
full stop
comma   full stop
comma
comma   full stop
comma   comma
comma
full stop   comma
full stop   colon
comma
comma   comma
full stop

full stop
full stop
full stop
comma   comma
full stop   comma

full stop   full stop
em dash   full stop   comma
full stop

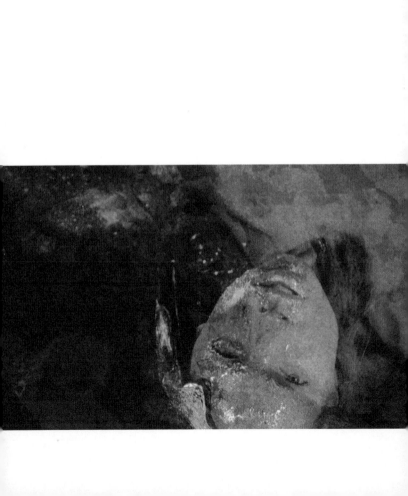

SWEET
ARE
THE
USES
OF
ADVERSITY

Be assured, your indolence will find its
twin in torture.

Oh, and a box of matches.

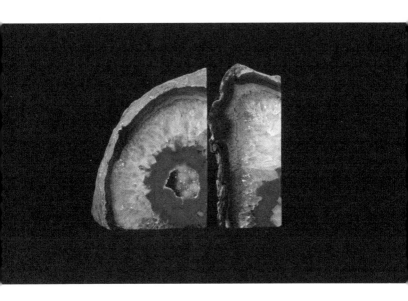

I know it needs to be done—it's just that
I don't like anyone touching me.

Yes, it's broken down again. Third time
in as many months. And not much more
than a year old.

But it clearly says on the window you
close at 5.00 pm. What, earlier on
Thursdays? I don't understand how
it ended up in my basket.

Sorry, this isn't flushing properly.

I can't see at all well from here, plus those two in front keep jiggling around in their seats. Let's move now before it gets too busy. No, I don't want to swap with you —I'd prefer to move.

This is almost cold. How's yours?

I slept so badly last night. The traffic noise from outside. Non-stop. Sirens. Music so loud — booming — I could even hear the chassis vibrating. Sirens. Cars going far too fast, then hitting a red light, screeching to stop in time. Lorries delivering who knows what. Sirens. Police. Ambulances. Fire engines. Sirens. Where are they all going?

I didn't *say* I know everything, but I am
usually right about things like this.

It's the big tooth at the back on the left-hand side. Yes, it's been sore for a month or so now, I was waiting for it to go away, sort of like a metallic twanging pain... When I chew on something hard... No, not that sensitive to heat or cold.

A FILM BY URSULA MAYER

STARRING
VALENTIJN DE HINGH

AND
NINA BRAUNSTEINER
JOACHIM GRAM
CARSON MCCOLL
NOVA

PRODUCER
JO GROSS

WRITER
MARIA FUSCO

DIRECTOR OF PHOTOGRAPHY
MARGARET SALMON

PRODUCTION MANAGER
TINA SHAND

PRODUCTION DESIGNER
LUCIE WILKINS

CLAPPER LOADER
WARREN MARKERT

WARDROBE SUPERVISOR
MEG ANDREW

WARDROBE ASSISTANT
STEVIE HOCKADAY

GOLD DRESS BY GARETH PUGH

HAIR & MAKE-UP ARTIST
GIADA VENTURINI

HAIR ASSISTANT
JIN JIN HELEN ONG

STILLS PHOTOGRAPHER
CAT STEVENS

RUNNER
KATARZYNA JANDER

EDITORS
URSULA MAYER
VINAY CHOWDHRY

ONLINE EDITOR
SUE GIOVANNI

GRAPHICS
WOLFRAM WIEDNER

MUSIC
SULLOM VOE
SEBASTIAN JIRO SCHLECHT
CHARLIE LOOKER

SOUND RECORDIST & DESIGN
CHRISTIANO SOSSI

SPECIAL THANKS TO

BERNADETTE BUCKLEY
ELE CARPENTER
ANNA COLIN
KRISTEN KREIDER
PATRICIA MACCORMACK
PIETERNEL VERMOORTEL
MARIA WALSH
ISLA LEAVER-YAP
DINO WIELAND

FOR FILM LONDON

HEAD OF PRODUCTION AND TALENT DEVELOPMENT
MAGGIE ELLIS

FLAMIN MANAGER
ROSE CUPIT

PRODUCTION ADVISOR
PINKY GHUNDALE

FUNDED BY ARTS COUNCIL ENGLAND THROUGH
FILM LONDON ARTISTS' MOVING IMAGE NETWORK

AUSTRIAN FEDERAL MINISTRY OF EDUCATION, ARTS AND CULTURE

THE ELEPHANT TRUST

Gonda is informed by Ayn Rand's 1934 play *Ideal*. In the script, controversial Russian American writer and philosopher Rand lays out her philosophical system of 'Objectivism' with its stubbornly anti-altruistic and individualistic position. As a critical counter to Rand's position, *Gonda* addresses cinematic and linguistic registers by creating kaleidoscopic spaces in which image, text, and sound shift roles to affect presupposed ideals of identity and existence. Noting how the cinematic image actually gazes back on us, the film utilises highly stylised and precisely composed floating imagery. *Gonda* experiments in polyphonic monologue embodied in the eponymous main character, Gonda, portrayed by Dutch transgender model Valentijn de Hingh.

The screenplay was developed from a series of interdisciplinary workshops which included academics, curators, critics, and writers who were invited to creatively respond to scenes from *Ideal*. The workshops centred on the possibilities of writing *through* or *by* rather than *about* Rand's play. The screenplay's key structural textual reference is the production structure of Félix Guattari's unrealised 1986 *Project for a Film by Kafka*, in which Guattari proposed a made-for-television cultural mini-series inspired by episodes in Kafka's writings and life. *Gonda*'s final screenplay cannibalises new writing and transcribed workshop material together with five letter-based passages from *Ideal*, nudging them into alternative personal pronouns, to make *Gonda* a film of voices.

Gonda is a thirty-minute 16 mm film directed by Ursula Mayer with a screenplay by Maria Fusco, and commissioned by Film London.

Published by Sternberg Press

Copyeditor Leah Whitman-Salkin
Proofreader Max Bach
Design A Practice for Everyday Life
Printing and binding fgb. freiburger graphische betriebe

Publication supported by
Bundesministerium für Unterricht,
Kunst und Kultur, Österreich;
Juliètte Jongma, Amsterdam;
and Monitor, Rome.
Thanks to Bettina Steinbrügge.

ISBN 978-3-943365-32-0

Sternberg Press
Caroline Schneider
Karl-Marx-Allee 78
D-10243 Berlin
www.sternberg-press.com